reflies
tage 8
aura Sharp

Teaching Notes

Contents

Introduction

Fireflies is an exciting non-fiction series within *Oxford Reading Tree*. The books are specially designed to be used alongside the Stage 8 stories. They provide practice of reading skills in a non-fiction context whilst using the same simple, repetitive sentences as the *Oxford Reading Tree* stories. They also contain a selection of high frequency vocabulary. Each stage builds on the reading skills and vocabulary from previous stages, and helps children to read with growing confidence. As children read these books, they should be encouraged to read independently through: using their knowledge of letter sounds; learning to recognize high frequency words on sight; using the pictures and the sense of the story to work out new vocabulary.

To help children approach each new book in this stage with confidence, prepare the children for reading by talking about the book, asking questions and using these Teacher's Notes and the additional *Guided Reading Cards* and *Take-Home Cards*.

How to introduce the books

Before reading the book, always read the title and talk about the picture on the cover. Go through the book together, looking at the pictures and talking about them. If there are words that are new or unfamiliar, point them out and read them with the children.

This booklet provides suggestions for using the books with groups of children or individuals. You can use the ideas with shared, group or guided reading sessions, or with individual children. Suggestions are also provided for writing, speaking and listening and cross-curricular links. You can use these suggestions to follow on from your reading, or use at another time.

Guided Reading Cards are available for each book. These provide more detailed guidance for using the books for guided reading. *Take-Home Cards* are also available for each book. These provide prompts and suggestions for parents reading with their children. You can store the relevant card with each book in your "Take-Home" selection of titles.

Vocabulary chart

Title	Vocabulary	Sounds	Bookband Level
Shipwrecks	there were these down people water much	'air' (there) 'or' (warm) 'er' (disaster, captured, were, boiler)	4 white
Modern Day Explorer: Steve Fossett	January August June December because when what first flight again	'er' (first, modern, explorer, world)	10 white
Ice-Maker, Ice-Breaker	your called water would could that there making sea	'er' (iceberg, water)	9 gold
Freaky Fish	their some about very night many water tree	'ea' (head), 'ea' (freaky, seahorse, beak, speed, treefish), 'oo' (kangaroo, food)	8 purple
Musician: Vanessa-Mae	one three five seven nine first people play	'ou' (young), 'oo' (wood, good), 'ou' sound, 'ai' (play, Mae)	10 white
What's Inside Me?	have these called make(s) take(s) many don't people help blood pulls pushes	'ou' (would) 'ear' (ear)	10 white

Teaching objectives

	Teacher's Notes			Guided Reading Cards
	Speaking and listening	Reading	Writing	Reading
Shipwrecks				
Scotland	Listening/Talking Level A/B	Level A/B	Level A/B	Level A/B
N. Ireland	Activities a, b, c, f, g, h, i Outcomes a, b, c, d, f, g, i	Activities a, b Outcomes b, c, d, e	Opportunities a Outcomes b	Activities a, b Outcomes b, c, d, e
Wales	Oracy Range 1, 2, 3, 5 Skills 1, 2, 3, 4, 5, 6	Range 1, 2, 3 Skills 1, 2, 4	Range 1, 2, 4 Skills 1, 4	Range 1, 2, 3 Skills 1, 2
NC/NLS Y2T3	1a-f 4b	T2 T16 T19 S6 W10	T19	T2 T16 T19 S6
Modern Day Explorer: Steve Fossett				
Scotland	Listening/Talking Level A/B	Level A/B	Level A/B	Level A/B
N. Ireland	Activities a, f, g, h, i Outcomes a, b, c, d, f, g, i	Activities a, b Outcomes b, c, d, e	Opportunities a Outcomes b	Activities a, b Outcomes b, c, d, e
Wales	Oracy Range 1, 2, 3, 5 Skills 1, 2, 3, 4, 5, 6	Range 1, 2, 3 Skills 1, 2, 4	Range 1, 2, 4 Skills 1, 4	Range 1, 2, 3 Skills 1, 2
NC/NLS Y2T3	1a-f 2c 2e	T2 T16 T17 S6 W4 W5	T19	T2 T17 S6
Ice-Maker, Ice-Breaker				
Scotland	Listening/Talking Level A/B	Level A/B	Level A/B	Level A/B
N. Ireland	Activities a, f, g, i Outcomes a, b, e, h	Activities a, b Outcomes b, c, d, e, h	Opportunities a Outcomes b	Activities a, b Outcomes b, c, d, e, h
Wales	Oracy Range 1, 2, 3, 5 Skills 1, 2, 3, 4, 5, 6	Range 1, 2, 3 Skills 1, 2, 4	Range 1, 2, 4 Skills 1, 4	Range 1, 2, 3 Skills 1, 2, 4
NC/NLS Y2T3	1a-f 3a	T15 S1 S7 W9	T19	T2 T15 W9
Freaky Fish				
Scotland	Listening/Talking Level A/B	Level A/B	Level A/B	Level A/B
N. Ireland	Activities a, f, g, i Outcomes a, b, c, d, e, g, h, i	Activities a, b Outcomes b, c, d	Opportunities a Outcomes b	Activities a, b Outcomes b, c, d, e
Wales	Oracy Range 1, 2, 3, 5 Skills 1, 2, 3, 4, 5, 6	Range 1, 2, 3 Skills 1, 2, 4	Range 1, 2, 4 Skills 1, 4, 5, 7	Range 1, 2, 3 Skills 1, 2
NC/NLS Y2T3	3a-e	T2 T16 S6 W9	T14	T2 T14 T16

Musician: Vanessa-Mae				
Scotland	Listening/Talking Level A/B	Level A/B	Level A/B	Level A/B
N. Ireland	Activities a, b, c, f, g, i Outcomes a, b, c, e, f, g, i	Activities a, b Outcomes b, c, d, e	Opportunities a Outcomes b	Activities a, b Outcomes b, c, d, e
Wales	Oracy Range 1, 2, 5 Skills 1, 2	Range 1, 2 Skills 1, 2	Range 1, 2, 4 Skills 1, 2, 4	Range 1, 2, 3 Skills 1, 2
NC/NLS Y2T3	1a-f 2d 3a 3 d-e	T2 T19 S1 S3 W2 W9	T19	T2 T19 W9
What's Inside Me?				
Scotland	Listening/Talking Level A/B	Level A/B	Level A/B	Level A/B
N. Ireland	Activities a, b, c, e, f, g, h, i Outcomes a, b, c, e, f, g, i	Activities a, b Outcomes b, c, d	Opportunities a Outcomes b	Activities a, b Outcomes b, c, d, e
Wales	Oracy Range 1, 2, 3, 5 Skills 1, 2, 3, 4, 5, 6	Range 1, 2, 3 Skills 1, 2, 4	Range 1, 2, 3 Skills 1, 2, 4, 5	Range 1, 2, 3 Skills 1, 2
NC/NLS Y2T3	1a-f	T14 T15 T16 T20 S7 W9	T19	T2 T14 T16

Shipwrecks

Reading the book with individuals or guided reading groups

NB for additional and more detailed guidance on guided reading see Stage 8 Guided Reading cards (available separately, ISBN 0199198039). Take-Home Cards are also available, providing guidance for parents/carers (ISBN 0199198020).

Introducing the book

- Before handing out the books, discuss the term "shipwreck" with the children. Ask the children to predict what sort of information we might find in a book about shipwrecks.
- Distribute the books and ask the children to skim-read the Contents page. Were their predictions accurate?
- Ask, "What will the Glossary tell us?"
- Read the introduction on pages 3 and 4, with the children following as you read. Ensure children understand the technical vocabulary "collisions", "navigating".
- Demonstrate using the Glossary for "weather reports".

During reading

Prepare:
questions about contents of pages 13 and 14, e.g.
What was the name of the ship wrecked by ice?
How long were the crew on board the ship?
What happened to the ship?

- Return to the Contents page and demonstrate scanning to find the "Shipwrecked by Ice" page.
- Turn to page 13. (Some children may be familiar with the *Ice-Maker, Ice-Breaker* book about icebergs.)
- Display the prepared questions we want to find answers to. Explain that in order to remember the information, we are going to make notes.
- Using pages 20 and 21, ask children to scan to find the information to answer the questions. Provide a model for making notes, e.g.

Book:		Page nos.
question	notes	

- Ask children to read a section of their choice and make notes accordingly.

Observing Check that the children:
  - make brief notes and do not copy chunks of text (T19)
  - use context cues and reading on and back to aid understanding of what is read (T2)

After reading
- Ask the children to refer to their notes and report back on the section they have chosen.
- Ask the children a question and get them to scan the relevant page for the answer.

Group and independent reading activities

Text level work

Objective Make sense of what is read using a variety of cues (T2)
Scan to find specific information (T16)
Make notes (T19)

- Ask children to scan-read to answer the following questions:
  When did these shipwrecks happen?
  Where were the ships wrecked?
- Ensure that the children make notes and encourage the use of a variety of formats, e.g. charts, diagrams, tables.

Sentence level work

Objective Turn statements into questions learning a range of words typically used to open questions (S6)

Prepare:
question word cards – When? What? Where? How? Who? Why?
a variety of statements taken from the text, e.g. page 9 "On the night of July 10th, the *Rainbow Warrior* was blown up in Auckland Harbour."

- Ask the children to turn the statements into questions, using the question cards.

Word level work

Objective Use synonyms to express similar meaning (W10)

Prepare:
a variety of written statements from text; dictionaries

- Highlight the key vocabulary and phrases in the statements.
- Ask the children to generate words or phrases that could substitute the given words,

e.g. "blown up"	destroyed
"tried to make a break"	escape
"spectacular"	wonderful

Speaking and listening activities for groups

Objectives 1a) speak with clear diction and appropriate intonation; 1b) choose words with precision; 1c) organize what they say; 1d) focus on the main point(s); 1e) include relevant detail;1f) take into account the needs of their listeners; 4b) create and sustain roles individually and when working with others

- Ask children to work in pairs and read the relevant pages for one of the shipwrecks.
  Imagine you are a newsreader. Prepare a news bulletin for the rest of the class about the shipwreck.
  Teachers could provide a series of sentence starters to support children, e.g. "Good evening viewers ..."
  "We have just had a report from ..."

Cross-curricular links
◀▶ **ICT (QCA 2E)**
Questions and answers
History (QCA 4 and 5)
Florence Nightingale; Great Fire of London

Writing

Objective To make simple notes (T19)

- Make further notes on other shipwrecks.
- Encourage the children to devise their own notes, make a chart and present it to the group and report back.
- Make an additional Glossary for key vocabulary that is not included in the book's Glossary.

Modern Day Explorer: Steve Fossett

Reading the book with individuals or guided reading groups

NB for additional and more detailed guidance on guided reading see Stage 8 Guided Reading cards (available separately, ISBN 0199198039). Take-Home Cards are also available, providing guidance for parents/carers (ISBN 0199198020).

Introducing the book

- Look at title of the book with the children and ask questions, such as: What does the word "explorer" mean to you? Do you know a word that is similar? (e.g. "exploring") What does the term "modern day" mean?
- Uncover the picture. Read the blurb on the back cover with children. What do they think this explorer "explores"?
- Skim-read the book with children. Point out the organizational features such as headings, information boxes, and bubbles.
- Read the introduction with the children (pages 3–5).

During reading

Prepare:

questions written up for the children to refer to while reading, e.g.:
What was the name of the balloon Steve Fossett used in his second attempt to fly around the world?
What caused Steve Fossett to crash land on his second attempt?
How do you think he felt when he crashed again?

- Ask the children to read from pages 6–11. Ask them to think about specific questions whilst they are reading the text.

Observing Check that the children:

- use the features of the text to aid their skim-reading, i.e. headings, subheadings, captions, and information boxes (T16)
- are able to skim-read to get the gist of the book and are not reading whole sections of text (T17)

After reading

- Refer children back to the prepared questions and ask for responses.
- Referring to the text, demonstrate how making notes can help us to remember information. This can be done in a variety of ways, e.g. a spidergram or information grid.

Group and independent reading activities

Text level work

Objectives Make sense of what is read using a variety of cues (T2)
Skim-read to speculate about a book (T17)

- Demonstrate how to skim-read to get a sense of how the text is structured and of its content. Skim-read up to page 12 with the children following your demonstration. Ask the children what they observed you doing.
- Ask children to do the same for the following pages in pairs, "demonstrating" skimming a text to a partner or to you. Set a limited time to do this. Ask children to "summarize" each page using only a word or phrase.
- Ensure the children tackle unknown vocabulary using a variety of cues. Ask children if any words gave them problems. If so, how did they tackle that word?

Sentence level work

Objective Turn statements into questions learning a range of words typically used to open questions (S6)

Prepare:
question word cards – What? Where? When? Why? How? Who?
a variety of written statements from the text, e.g. "He had to land in a mustard field in northern India." (page 10)

- Encourage the children to turn the statements into questions orally.
- Note down the question words used so that the children can read them.

Word level work

Objective To read on sight high frequency words from Appendix 1 and graded texts (W4, W5)

Prepare:
question word cards or words on computer screen or SMARTboard
a sheet with list of words (1 per child)

ordinal number word cards up to "seventh"
names of balloon craft

- Look at the question word cards. Ask children:
  What is similar about spelling? What is different?
  Which bit(s) might give you problems?
- Underline or highlight these on your list of words.
- Give the children 2 minutes to practise the "look-say-cover-write" method with words.
- Using the word cards, show a word for 10 seconds to the children and then ask children to write the word on the whiteboard. Ask them to check their own spelling. Circle any part that was incorrect. Write the word again.
- Look at ordinal number word cards. Use in the same way as the question words activities.
- Match word cards to balloon names, e.g.

First	balloon was called	Solo Challenger
Second	balloon was called	Solo Spirit

Speaking and listening activities for groups

Objectives 1a) speak with clear diction and appropriate intonation; 1b) choose words with precision; 1c) organize what they say; 1d) focus on the main point(s); 1e) include relevant detail;1f) take into account the needs of their listeners; 2c) make relevant comments; 2e) ask questions to clarify their understanding

- Ask the children to imagine they are going to interview Steve Fossett and to compose some questions to ask.
- When completing the information grid, ensure that the children explain their answers fully and that their responses are relevant.

◀▶ **Cross-curricular links**
Geography (QCA 5) Where in the world is Barnaby Bear?
Maths (NNS Framework) Number, charts and graphs

Writing

Objective To make simple notes (T19)

- Ask children to devise a grid or chart to make notes on, e.g. where Fosset landed and the distance he flew each time.

Ice-Maker, Ice-Breaker

Reading the book with individuals or guided reading groups

NB for additional and more detailed guidance on guided reading see Stage 8 Guided Reading cards (available separately, ISBN 0199198039). Take-Home Cards are also available, providing guidance for parents/carers (ISBN 0199198020).

Introducing the book

Prepare:
a reading chart (large enough for the group to see), as shown below

- Read the blurb on the back cover with the children.
- On a before/after reading grid answer, "What do we know about icebergs?"

Book: What we know:	
Before reading	After reading

- Direct the children to the Contents page. Demonstrate locating a page for a specific topic. Ask children to locate other topic pages using the Contents page.

During reading

- Give children a list of topics from the Contents page (up to page 16 and not in numerical order). Observe how they locate the page and read the text.

Observing   Check that the children:

- know the difference between a Contents page and an Index page and when to use them (T15)
- are using punctuation in the text accurately to aid fluency in their reading (S1)

After reading

Prepare

a reading chart (see above)
true/false statements about information in the book, written on cards

- Return to the chart with the children.
  What do we know about icebergs after our reading?
  Were we correct in what we thought before we read the text?
- Ask the children to sort the true/false statement cards into appropriate groups. Encourage them to refer back to the text to check.

Group and independent reading activities

Text level work

Objective Use Contents and Index pages (T15)

- Discuss the layout of the Index page. Compare this to the Contents page.
- Read page 16 with the children. Explain that the following pages of the book will give them information about special ships that break up ice – ice-breakers.
- Ask children to note down the key words that give information about ice-breaker ships.
- Give information about the *Titanic*.

Sentence level work

Objective Question comparison (S7)

- Using pages 3–13, find question statements. Ask, "How are questions started?"
  Make a collection, e.g.
  > Which pole …?
  > What is …?
  > Do you think …?
  > What happens when …?
  > Does it …?
- Ask the children to compose orally their own questions about icebergs using the information they have read.

Word level work

Objective To extend vocabulary, new words linked to reading (W9)

- Locate the words "ice" and "ocean". What do children notice about the grapheme "c" in each word? The "c" is soft, making an "s" sound.
- Locate interesting vocabulary in text, e.g."cargo ship", "hull", "passenger ship", "unsinkable".
- Check the children's understanding of these terms, using a dictionary if appropriate.

Speaking and listening activities for groups

Objectives 1a) speak with clear diction and appropriate intonation; 1b) choose words with precision; 1c) organize what they say; 1d) focus on the main point(s); 1e) include relevant detail; 1f) take into account the needs of their listeners; 3a) take turns in speaking

Prepare:
statements (true and false about icebergs)
a sorting chart (with headings: agree, disagree)

- Ask the children to explain how icebergs are formed in oceans. Ensure they use appropriate vocabulary and include relevant details.
- Play the "Agree/Disagree" game. Ask the children to sort the true and false statements into the appropriate categories.

Cross-curricular links
◀▶ **Geography (QCA 17)** Global eye
ICT (QCA 2C) Finding information
Science (QCA 2D) Grouping and changing materials

Writing

Objective To make simple notes (T19)

- List the key words in a section of the text, e.g. pages 18–19. Ask the children to create a Glossary for the key words.
- Encourage the children to make a flow-chart diagram of instructions for making your own iceberg at home.

Freaky Fish

Reading the book with individuals or guided reading groups

NB for additional and more detailed guidance on guided reading see Stage 8 Guided Reading cards (available separately, ISBN 0199198039). Take-Home Cards are also available, providing guidance for parents/carers (ISBN 0199198020).

Introducing the book

- Question the children about the meaning of the word "Freaky" in the title.
- Look at the Contents page and read together the names of the fish.
- Point out specific vocabulary and locate it on the page with children, e.g. "camouflage", "ferocious"; and encourage the use of context and graphic cues to determine the meanings.

During reading

- Choose one species of fish to demonstrate scanning text to find specific information about its appearance.
- Ask the children to do the same for another species.
- Ask the children to read on, scanning for information about the appearance of the other fish. Check that new vocabulary is understood by inviting children to explain the meanings of words.

Observing Check that the children:

- use and cross-check reading strategies to read unfamiliar words and to determine their meaning, e.g. "camouflage" (T2)
- scan-read for specific information using key words (T16)

After reading

- Ask children to scan-read two species pages to find specific information about fish that use camouflage as protection.
- Using question cards – What? Where? Why? How? Which? – ask the children to compose (orally) a question about a fish for the group/class to answer, e.g. How does the stargazer keep away its enemies?

Group and independent reading activities

Text level work

Objective To scan a text to find specific information (T16)

- Ask the children to scan-read to find species of fish that use spines to scare their enemies. Ask, "Which is the key word to locate?" (spines)

Sentence level work

Objective To turn statements into questions, learning a range of words typically used to open questions (S6)

Prepare:
cards with fish names
cards with question words

- One child takes a "fish" card and all the children locate the relevant page in the book. Each child in the group takes a question card. They then ask questions about the chosen fish using their question word, e.g. "Why are the spines of the lionfish deadly?", "Where do lionfish live?", "How do lionfish catch their food?" The fish-card-holder answers the questions, referring to text.

Word level work

Objective To extend vocabulary, learn new words linked to reading (W9)

Prepare:
cards or self-adhesive notes with key vocabulary from the book

- Ask children to use the chosen word in a sentence, orally.

  Prepare: cards or self-adhesive notes with the fish names: "stargazer", "lionfish", "seahorse"

- Cut up the fish-name cards into the two parts (star/gazer, lion/fish, sea/horse). Ask children to combine two cards to make up some imaginary "fish names". Emphasize new words made out of two existing words. Encourage experimentation, e.g. "seagazer", "lionhorse", "starhorse".

Speaking and listening activities for groups

Objectives 3a) take turns in speaking; 3b) relate their contributions to what has gone on before; 3c) take different views into account; 3d) extend their ideas in the light of discussion; 3e) give reasons for opinions

- In paired/group work encourage the children to respond to others' contributions by clarifying, rephrasing and questioning.

◄► *Cross-curricular links*
Science (QCA 2B and 2C)
Plants and animals in the local environment
Geography (QCA 4)
Moving and growing

Writing

Objective To pose questions (T14)

Prepare:
a flipchart with a prompt question on it, e.g. "What else do you want to know about the … fish?"

- Using question word cards as above, ask the children to compose two more questions about one of the fish they have read about and to write them down.

Musician: Vanessa-Mae

Reading the book with individuals or guided reading groups

NB for additional and more detailed guidance on guided reading see Stage 8 Guided Reading cards (available separately, ISBN 0199198039). Take-Home Cards are also available, providing guidance for parents/carers (ISBN 0199198020).

Introducing the book

- Look at the front cover together and read the title aloud to the children.
- Ask the children to predict what the book will be about. Encourage them to look at the cover illustration and at the word "musician" in the title. Can they see a smaller word "music" inside?
- Ask the children if they know any other musicians and note their responses.
- Read the blurb on the back cover of the book to confirm what the book is about.
- Skim through the book with the children, pointing out the section headings.
- Introduce some key vocabulary which may be unfamiliar to the children, e.g. orchestra, manuscript, microphone.

During reading

- Encourage children to use all of the reading strategies they have learned to work out unknown vocabulary and to check what they have read makes sense. Remind them to look for words they know within words.
- As they read, ask the children to make simple notes on three facts they have read specifically about Vanessa-Mae.

Observing Check that the children:

- are using phonic and context cues to work out unknown vocabulary (T2)
- are using punctuation to aid fluent reading and reading for meaning (S1)

After reading

- Ask the children to share the three facts they found out about Vanessa-Mae.
- Ask the children to discuss what other subjects they have found out about as they read the book, e.g. making violins, parts of a violin, writing down music, piano and orchestra.

Group and independent reading activities

Text level work

Objective To make simple notes (T19)

- Ask the children to make notes on how a violin is made. Share and compare their notes with a partner. Remind them to locate the correct section in the book by using the Contents page headings.

Sentence level work

Objective To use verb tenses (S3)

Prepare:
copies of a 3-column grid with the words "plays", "playing" and "played" written along the top and the following sentences from pages 3 and 4, copied onto individual strips of paper:

Vanessa-Mae plays the violin.
At the age of nine she first played the violin in public.
Vanessa-Mae started playing the piano when she was three.

- What do the children notice about the three words on the grid? What is the same? What is different?
- Show them the sentences on the strips of paper. Cut up the sentences to isolate the verb "play" in each sentence. Separate these from the sentences.
- Ask the children to put in the correct word to complete the sentence. Encourage them to re-read the sentence to make sure it makes sense.
- Using a set of root words taken from the book (e.g. "join", "need", "call", "hold"), ask the children to complete the grid to make up the sets of words, e.g.

play	plays	played	playing
join	joins	joined	joining

Word level work

Objective To discriminate syllables in words (W2)

- Using words taken from the book, count the number of syllables in the word with the children, e.g. vi/o/lin (3), pop (1), mus/ic (2).
- Ask the children to use the book to find other words with 1, 2, and 3 syllables and to write them on small cards and group them.

Objective To extend vocabulary (W9)

- Ensure children understand the following words and phrases used in the book: "violinist", "perform", "engineer", "in public", "manuscript", "microphone", "classical music", "composing".

Speaking and listening activities for groups

Objectives 1a) speak with clear diction and appropriate intonation; 1b) choose words with precision; 1c) organize what they say; 1f) take into account the needs of their listeners; 2d) listen to others' reactions; 3a) take turns in speaking; 3b) relate their contributions to what has gone on before; 3d) extend their ideas in the light of discussion; 3e) give reasons for opinions and actions

- Read the "Playing the Violin" section on page 19 with the children. Ask the children to prepare how to demonstrate this to a group and to explain what they are doing as they demonstrate.

Cross-curricular links
◀▶ **Music (QCA 1)** Ongoing skills; **(QCA 2)** Sounds interesting; **(QCA 6)** What's the score?
Science (QCA 1F) Sound and hearing

Writing

Objectives To make simple notes (T19)

- Ask the children to read pages 5–7. What does this tell us about? (The differences between a violin and a piano.)
- Ask the children to make notes on the similarities and differences between the two instruments.

What's Inside Me?

Reading the book with individuals or guided reading groups

NB for additional and more detailed guidance on guided reading see Stage 8 Guided Reading cards (available separately, ISBN 0199198039). Take-Home Cards are also available, providing guidance for parents/carers (ISBN 0199198020).

Introducing the book

- Discuss the title of the book. What do children think they will be finding out about in this text?
- Introduce the term "explanation". The title asks a question and the book will give an explanation.
- Model the process of skimming through the book for an overall sense of the content as the children follow using their own copy of the book. Ask the children to repeat the process and summarize what they have gleaned from a "very quick read through". Emphasize that this is to give them a rough idea of the content, not detailed knowledge.
- Display a question you want to find the answer to. Demonstrate scan-reading to retrieve the specific information for the answer.
- Discuss with children the purpose of the "Did you know...?" sections.

During reading

- Ask children to skim-read for an overall sense of the presentational features, e.g. captions, headings, subheadings, illustrations, information boxes, variety of print styles.
- Direct the children to the Contents page. Choose one topic to scan-read for specific information, e.g. about the heart. Observe whether the children use the Contents page to locate the page and if they scan the page to retrieve the information.

Observing Check that the children:

- ■ use the Contents list to locate a specific topic (T15)
- ■ recognize and can name the presentational features used in the book – captions, headings, subheadings and information boxes (T20)

After reading

- On an outline drawing of a person, label the body parts you have just read about. Show them how to set out the drawing.
- Refer to the "Did you know?" box in each section. Note how a fact is given but in question form.
- Compose some other "Did you know?" facts for each section using information found in the text.

Group and independent reading activities

Text level work

Objectives To pose questions (T14)
To scan to find specific information (T16)

- Prior to reading, model how to compose a question. Ask the children to pose a question about one part of the body that they will read about. Record their questions on a flipchart to refer back to after reading.
- Refer to pages 8 and 9. Ask the children to scan-read for veins and arteries. Discuss key words in the text box on page 8.

Sentence level work

Objective To compare a variety of question forms (S7)

Prepare:
question cards – Who? What? Where? When? Why? Which?

- Refer to the "Did you know?" boxes. Ask the children to use the cards to rephrase the questions into question and answer cards, e.g. What is the strongest muscle in the body? (page 15); How many muscles do you use when you smile? (page 17)

Word level work

Objective To extend vocabulary (W9)

Prepare:
a word and meaning chart, e.g.

word	meaning
biceps	
veins	
muscles	
inhalation	

- Using context clues and referring to the text, complete the chart. This could be prepared on the computer to link with ICT activities.

Speaking and listening activities for groups

Objectives 1a) speak with clear diction and appropriate intonation; 1b) choose words with precision; 1c) organize what they say; 1d) focus on the main point(s); 1e) include relevant detail; 1f) take into account the needs of their listeners

- Using an outline drawing of a human, ask children to explain in their own words how blood travels through the body.

Cross-curricular links
◄► **Science (QCA 2A)** Health and growth
ICT (QCA 2E) Questions and answers
Art (QCA 1A) Self portrait

Writing

Objective To write non-fiction text using texts read as models (T19)

Prepare:
one full-length portrait drawn on an A4-size sheet for each child
an outline of a person on a second A4 sheet with the parts of the body drawn on and labelled

- Encourage the children to join the sheets together to make a book with the portrait as the top sheet, e.g.

Self portrait	Diagram of body parts

- Show the children how to make fact cards and create a lift-the-flap page – two sheets of paper the same size divided into identical boxes. Write the key vocabulary on one sheet and then cut around each box.
- Write a sentence or a question on the underneath sheet in the relevant box. Give the page in the book to refer to.

Links to other Oxford Reading Tree titles

Fireflies Stage 8	Oxford Reading Tree stories with similar subjects/themes
Shipwrecks	The Treasure Chest, Mirror Island, The Holiday, ORT True Stories – Titanic Survivor, Arctic Hero, Travels with Magellan, Ocean Adventure
Modern Day Explorer: Steve Fossett	Mirror Island, Lost in the Jungle, ORT True Stories – Titanic Survivor, Arctic Hero, Travels with Magellan, Ocean Adventure, Man on the Moon, High Flier, At the Top of the World
Ice-Maker, Ice-Breaker	The Treasure Chest, Mirror Island, ORT True Stories – Titanic Survivor, Arctic Hero
Freaky Fish	The Treasure Chest, Submarine Adventure
Musician: Vanessa-Mae	The Finest in the Land, Robin Hood, William and the Pied Piper and Hamid Does His Best
What's Inside Me?	The Emergency

OXFORD
UNIVERSITY PRESS

Great Clarendon Street, Oxford OX2 6DP

Oxford University Press is a department of the University of Oxford. It furthers the University's objective of excellence in research, scholarship, and education by publishing worldwide in

Oxford New York

Auckland Bangkok Buenos Aires Cape Town Chennai Dar es Salaam Delhi Hong Kong Istanbul Karachi Kolkata Kuala Lumpur Madrid Melbourne Mexico City Mumbai Nairobi São Paulo Shanghai Taipei Tokyo Toronto

Oxford is a registered trade mark of Oxford University Press in the UK and in certain other countries

© Oxford University Press 2003

The moral rights of the author have been asserted

Database right Oxford University Press (maker)

First published 2003

British Library Cataloguing in Publication Data

Data available

Teacher's Notes: ISBN 0 19 919801 2

10 9 8 7 6 5 4 3 2

Page make-up by IFA Design Ltd, Plymouth, Devon

Printed in China through Colorcraft Ltd., Hong Kong